HANNAH
goes to
School

by Helen and Clive Dorman

Paediatric Consultant:
Dr Huw R Jenkins MA MD FRCP FRCPCH

CP Publishing

Let us say hello to Hannah and her class, and to the friends, teachers and helpers that she meets today.

Hello Teah, Danielle, Reema, Remmy, Steven, Carole, Jenny, Lucy, Hannah, Ellie, Ye Jee and Sam.

Hello Anthony, Kathy and Jessica.

Hello Barney. Barney helps with reading.

Hello Scott, James, Annamarie and Kristie.

Hello Mrs Lee.
Mrs Lee is the class
assistant.

Hello Miss Holt.
Miss Holt is the
class teacher.

Hello Mrs Gardner.
Mrs Gardner is the
dinner lady.

Hello Mr Brooker.
Mr Brooker is the
head teacher.

Let us turn the pages and find out what happens
at school today.

1 Hannah is having her breakfast. She is going to school today and that is why she is wearing her school uniform. Hannah is looking at the clock. She leaves the house at a quarter to nine, so that she is not late for school.

2 Daddy is taking Hannah to school. She lives near the school and they like to walk.
Hannah and her daddy talk about lots of things on the way.

What do you like for breakfast?
What do you think Hannah and her daddy talk about?

1 On the way to school they meet Kathy, Jessica and Anthony. Hannah went to the same nursery as Anthony but now they go to different schools. They are still good friends.

2 Anthony and Hannah have different badges on their uniforms.

3 Hannah looks at Anthony's school.

1 In school Annamarie greets Hannah with a hug.

2 Mrs Gardner blows the whistle at 9 o'clock. It is time for school to start.

3 Hannah says goodbye to her daddy and goes in the classroom.

4 She puts her lunch box with the others.

5 Then she puts her bag in her tray. Lucy is putting her teddy away where it is safe.

1 Miss Holt is taking the register. All the children must be quiet. She calls each child's name in turn to see if they are in class today.
When the children hear their name, they say, 'Good morning Miss Holt'.

Ellie and Remmy have been sitting very quietly. Sometimes, Remmy finds it difficult to sit still and Ellie feels she must say the words that come into her head before she forgets them.

3 Ellie and Remmy feel very proud to be chosen to take the register to the school office today.

1 The children line up at the door for assembly.
Miss Holt sees that not everyone is standing up
straight. She knows they find this hard to do.
Carole is leaning on Danielle. Teah and Ellie are
getting bored and have turned to chat to Steven who
is standing very well.
Sam is sad. He thinks he has done something wrong
and that he is why he is last in line. He has not.
Maybe he will be nearer the front of the line later
today.

Do you know what an assembly is?

1 After Mr Brooker has said hello to everyone they all sing a song together.
The children love to sing in assembly.

2 Today Mr Brooker gives an award to Hannah for helping Carole.

3 Remmy gets an award for sharing. Everyone claps. Sam feels better now he is with Miss Holt.

1 In the library, Barney, a school helper, is hearing Teah read.

2 Next he listens to Hannah read. He writes in her reading book how well she has read.

3 Miss Holt helps Teah and the rest of the reading group to choose different books.

4 Mrs Lee reads a book to Carole.
Carole loves books. She cannot read but she likes to turn the pages and look at the pictures.

1 Now Miss Holt plays a word game. She holds up a card with a word on it and the children try to tell her what it is. Steven does not feel like listening.

2 Steven now has his hand up. Miss Holt is pleased Steven is ready to join in the game.
The children find it difficult to concentrate all the time.

3 Next Miss Holt plays a game with numbers. Miss Holt has hidden four fingers. Danielle is counting the number of fingers Miss Holt has left.

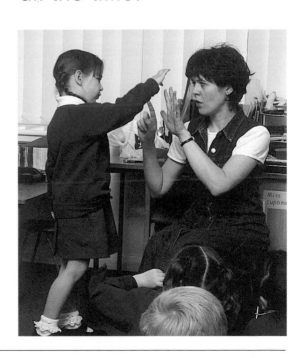

Can you count how many fingers are left?

1 The children settle down to do some drawing.

2 Reema has lots of things on the table and thinks she needs all the room.

3 Remmy wants to sit in the other seat. Reema doesn't want to share the space.

4 Remmy sits down next to her. Sometimes it is difficult to share.

5 Reema decides to join Lucy, Jenny, Teah and Danielle.

6 Everyone is working very hard. They are talking and sharing ideas.

7 Hannah tries to read a book to Ye Jee.

8 They find a loose page in the book. Miss Holt is helping them stick it back.

9 Hannah, Ye Jee and Mrs Lee have joined the groups.

10 Mrs Lee helps Steven with a puzzle. Carole is colouring.

11 Carole is using lots of colours for the horses.

12 Steven has nearly finished the puzzle. One piece to go!

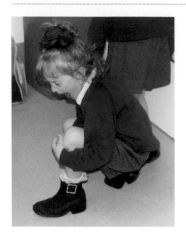

1 Poor Teah has just hurt herself.

2 Mrs Lee comforts Teah. What do you think Steven is thinking?

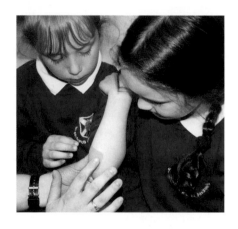

3 Teah is in the medical room with Hannah. Mrs Gardner is cleaning Teah's elbow.

4 She puts a plaster on it.

5 Mrs Gardner takes them back to the class. Hannah comforts Teah, who has been very brave.

1 Teah puts on an apron.

2 Teah, Reema, Lucy and Danielle are making and painting houses.

3 Outside, Jenny and Ellie are seeing what water can do. They chat and have fun finding out more and more.

4 Ellie looks for some soil to add to the water. She loves to experiment and often does more than she has been asked to do.

1 Lucy and Teah have washed their hands and are drying them before they go for their lunch.

2 The children who are having school dinners line up. Mrs Gardner serves the food. Annamarie pours the water.

3 The children take their food to sit with those who have packed lunches. Sam is enjoying his sandwich.

4 Mrs Gardner serves Scott and Annamarie with their lunch.

5 James is not sure if he likes the lettuce. Ellie and Kristie watch.

6 Mrs Lee helps Carole with her roll.

7 Hannah has packed lunch but sometimes she wishes she had school dinners because she likes pizza.

1 Sam tries to tell the girls what to do.

2 He wants to play 'chase'. Ellie is not sure.

3 Sam cannot ask Jenny to play so he pulls her.

4 Danielle copies Sam and pulls Ellie.

5 Eventually Ellie, Danielle, Jenny, Teah and Sam join in together to play 'chase'.

6 Ye Jee, Hannah and Lucy love to see Annamarie in the playground.

7 Hannah and Lucy have great fun hand-clapping!

8 Carole loves to drink from the water fountain.

9 Mrs Gardner blows the whistle. Playtime is over. The children will now go back to their classroom.

1 Miss Holt tells the class that it is storytime.
She has handed out cards with words on them.

2 When Miss Holt reads the story she asks the children to hold up the word if it is on their card.

3 Miss Holt begins to read the story.

4 Jenny holds her card up in the air.

1 Miss Holt prepares the children for group work.

2 Hannah and Ye Jee hand out the pencils.

3 They all try to think of words that rhyme.

4 Steven has a good idea.

5 Miss Holt and Hannah help Ye Jee with letters.

6 Hannah is writing her name on her work.

1 Teah is using the mouse at the computer.

2 Danielle is going through the story again.

3 Mrs Lee, Carole and Ellie are colouring.

4 Remmy is sticking.

5 When the children have finished, they like to show Miss Holt their work, usually all at once. Poor Miss Holt needs more eyes and ears! Well done Ellie! She is waiting her turn.

1 Now it is tidy up time.
Ye Jee collects the word
cards. Jenny is still
drawing.

2 Jenny finds it hard to
know when to finish.
Miss Holt helps her
make the decision.

3 Now Jenny can join in
the tidying up.

4 Miss Holt stops the class.
Steven is still tidying.

5 They play a game
before moving on to the
next lesson.

1 Teah, Steven and Hannah get their PE bags from their pegs.

2 Today Danielle does not feel like getting ready for PE.

3 Teah is puting her clothes down very neatly.

4 Ellie and Jenny have not got their PE kit. Miss Holt says they will have to choose a book instead.

5 Mrs Lee plays peek-a-boo with Carole! Jenny chooses a book.

6 When the children line up for PE they are always excited.

7 Mrs Gardner looks after Ellie and Jenny.

1 Lucy is learning control of the ball. The children take it in turns.

2 Mrs Lee guides Carole.

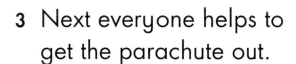

3 Next everyone helps to get the parachute out.

4 They all lift and lower the parachute together to try to keep the ball on the top. Oh, no! Not this time…

1 After the children have changed, they collect their bags and sit on the carpet. Miss Holt shows them the leaflet they will be taking home to give to their parents.

2 Hannah hands out the leaflets.

3 She then gets a star for writing her name neatly.

1 Jenny looks for her childminder.

2 Remmy looks for his mummy.

3 Ye Jee is called. Her mummy has arrived to collect her.

4 Now Danielle is called. The children leave one at a time.

5 Hannah's daddy has come to collect her. She has had a busy day at school today and has lots to tell him.

6 Back in the classroom Ellie and Teah are still waiting to be collected. It is getting late and Miss Holt hopes it will not be long before they too can go home.

Let us say bye bye to Hannah and her class, and to the friends, teachers and helpers that she met today.

Bye bye Teah, Danielle, Reema, Remmy, Steven, Carole, Jenny, Lucy, Hannah, Ellie, Ye Jee and Sam.

Bye bye Anthony, Kathy and Jessica.

Bye bye Barney. Barney helps with reading.

Bye bye Scott, James, Annamarie and Kristie.

Bye bye Mrs Lee.
Mrs Lee is the class
assistant.

Bye bye Miss Holt.
Miss Holt is the
class teacher.

Bye bye Mrs Gardner.
Mrs Gardner is the
dinner lady.

Bye bye Mr Brooker.
Mr Brooker is the
head teacher.

Starting school

Starting school is an exciting and emotional time for you and your child. She is becoming independent and eager to grow up, and starting school is the first major step towards that independence. For the first time your child will be advised and influenced for long periods of time by others and she will mix with a wide range of children with varying abilities and social skills. She will have to draw on her own resources to make decisions and deal with the consequences. Many children will have had the benefit of nursery, but not always in the school they will attend. Entering a strange environment with new faces, contact with more and older children, learning new routines and a longer time away from parents can be daunting for a young child.

Schools introduce children to their new environment in different ways. Some stagger intakes by age and/or begin with half days, building to full days, but all try to be sensitive to your child's needs.

Some children find starting school easy; others find it more difficult. Your child may breeze into the classroom without even a glance back or 'bye bye'. This may be as difficult for you as having a child that clings on, cries and refuses to let go. Other children settle well initially but when they realise this is a permanent arrangement they may decide it's not such a good idea after all and react in the opposite way. Whatever happens, your child *will* settle in time.

Settling into school

Reception class brings together a large number of children with varying backgrounds and abilities. They will jostle for friendships and attempt leadership roles within their peer group. Being young, they will not all have the emotional resources to say in words what they want or don't like. They may push, scratch, bite or snatch to get their point across: this is not acceptable in or out of school. The teacher will be aware of these incidents and deal with the issues as they arise. Always talk to your child and the teacher about any concerns. Also be aware that it may happen again if a new pupil enters the class, as this can be unsettling for everyone.

Settling into reception class

Reception class teaches important skills which will enable your child to settle into a structured, learning environment preparing her for the rest of her education. These skills are not just academic but social. There may be children in the class with special needs like disabilities or language differences. Understanding others through sharing, joining in and helping is important. The purpose of a reception class is not to enable your child to read and write in the first term but, by providing opportunities to learn through play, to help the teacher find out and develop your child's abilities.

School is an important place in the community

School is a shared place the community. Together the teachers', children's and parents' input into running the school are crucial in enabling every child to get the best enjoyment and educational benefit. If you can help with class activities or events it is not only a good way of making friends but also a way of understanding and sharing your child's life while in school.

Home and school

Children can find their early days at school very tiring: there are a lot of new things to take in. So don't feel upset if after picking her up you ask 'What did you do in school today?' and she says, 'I can't remember'. She will tell you when she is ready. At home your child may need to sleep or cry: this helps to process the information of the day and recharge the batteries.

About this book

Volunteers from Hannah's class have taken part in this book to give an overall view of life in school. The text has been written to include an insight into the feelings and common actions many children come across and may find difficult to control in the school environment. The children photographed may not themselves have had to deal with the situations in which they are portrayed. We also instigated some events to portray situations which highlight how teachers and parents can help deal with sensitive areas of possible conflict in and out of the classroom.

First published in 2000 by CP Publishing
Richmond, Surrey, United Kingdom

Text Copyright © 1999 Helen & Clive Dorman
Photographs Copyright © 1999 Helen Dorman
This edition Copyright © 2000 The Children's Project Ltd

ISBN 1 903275 06 7

Printed in Hong Kong

Acknowledgements
We would like to thank St Richard's with St Andrews C of E Primary School, Richmond, for their cooperation. Special thanks to Nick Brooker, Katharine Holt, Diane Lee, Eleanor Gardner, Kathy Blair and the children: Jessica, Anthony, Teah, Danielle, Reema, Remmy, Steven, Carole, Jenny, Lucy, Ellie, Ye Jee, Sam, Scott, James, Annamarie, Kristie and, of course, Hannah and brother Barney, who were all brilliant.